Guest Spot

Play-along for Violin
KIDS' MUSICALS

10.44

Published by
Wise Publications
14-15 Berners Street, London W1T 3LJ, UK.

Exclusive Distributors:
Music Sales Limited
Distribution Centre, Newmarket Road, Bury St Edmunds,
Suffolk IP33 3YB, UK.
Music Sales Pty Limited
120 Rothschild Avenue, Rosebery, NSW 2018, Australia.

Order No. AM995918
ISBN 13: 978-1-84772-814-2
This book © Copyright 2009 Wise Publications,
a division of Music Sales Limited.

Arranging and engravings supplied by Camden Music.
Edited by Fiona Bolton.
Compiled by Nick Crispin.

CD recorded, mixed and mastered by Jonas Persson.
Violin played by Michael Keelan.

Printed in the EU.

Your Guarantee of Quality:
As publishers, we strive to produce every book to
the highest commercial standards.
The music has been freshly engraved and the book has been
carefully designed to minimise awkward page turns and
to make playing from it a real pleasure.
Particular care has been given to specifying acid-free, neutral-sized
paper made from pulps which have not been elemental chlorine bleached.
This pulp is from farmed sustainable forests and was
produced with special regard for the environment.
Throughout, the printing and binding have been planned to
ensure a sturdy, attractive publication which should give years of enjoyment.
If your copy fails to meet our high standards,
please inform us and we will gladly replace it.

www.musicsales.com

Guest Spot

Play-along for Violin
KIDS' MUSICALS

Wise Publications
part of The Music Sales Group
London/New York/Paris/Sydney/Copenhagen/Berlin/Madrid/Tokyo

As Long As He Needs Me (from 'Oliver!')

Words & Music by Lionel Bart

Benjamin Calypso
(from 'Joseph And The Amazing Technicolor® Dreamcoat')

Words by Tim Rice
Music by Andrew Lloyd Webber

Breaking Free (from 'High School Musical On Stage!')

Words & Music by Jamie Houston

Expressively ♩ = 108

Chim Chim Cher-ee (from 'Mary Poppins')

Words & Music by Richard M. Sherman & Robert B. Sherman

15

Can You Feel The Love Tonight
(from 'The Lion King')

Words by Tim Rice
Music by Elton John

Electricity (from 'Billy Elliot: The Musical')

Words by Lee Hall
Music by Elton John

The Lonely Goatherd (from 'The Sound Of Music')

Words by Oscar Hammerstein II
Music by Richard Rodgers

So You Wanna Be A Boxer (from 'Bugsy Malone')

Words & Music by Paul Williams

Tomorrow (from 'Annie')

Words by Martin Charnin
Music by Charles Strouse

The Candy Man
(from 'Willy Wonka & The Chocolate Factory')

Words & Music by Leslie Bricusse & Anthony Newley

With a bright swing ♩ = 140

molto rit.

Meno mosso   rit.   A tempo ♩ = 116

rit.

1 2 3 4 5 6 7 8 9

CD Track Listing

Full instrumental performances...

1. Tuning notes

2. As Long As He Needs Me
(Bart) Lakeview Music Publishing Company Limited.

3. Benjamin Calypso
(Lloyd Webber/Rice) The Really Useful Group Limited.

4. Breaking Free
(Houston) Warner/Chappell Artemis Music.

5. Chim Chim Cher-ee
(Sherman/Sherman) Warner/Chappell Artemis Music.

6. Can You Feel The Love Tonight
(Rice/John) Warner/Chappell Artemis Music.

7. Electricity
(Hall/John) Universal Music Publishing Limited.

8. The Lonely Goatherd
(Rodgers/Hammerstein II) EMI Music Publishing Limited.

9. So You Wanna Be A Boxer
(Williams) Chappell Music Limited.

10. Tomorrow
(Charnin/Strouse) Warner/Chappell Music Limited.

11. The Candy Man
(Bricusse/Newley) Universal Music Publishing Limited.

Backing tracks only...

12. As Long As He Needs Me

13. Benjamin Calypso

14. Breaking Free

15. Chim Chim Cher-ee

16. Can You Feel The Love Tonight

17. Electricity

18. The Lonely Goatherd

19. So You Wanna Be A Boxer

20. Tomorrow

21. The Candy Man